'Truth is eternal, just like a diamond.'

DIAMONDS

Marijan Dundek

NOBLE GEMS INTERNATIONAL

NOBLE GEMS INTERNATIONAL

Copyright © Marijan Dundek

3rd revised edition published 2009: ISBN 978-0-9537884-3-9
    Reprinted 2010, 2011, 2013, 2015

1st edition published 1999: ISBN 09535371-0-2
2nd edition published 2002: ISBN 09535371-1-0

A CIP catalogue record for this book is available from the British Library

Edited by Denise Dresner
Designed by Pawel Starzak

Cover photo by Laurent Boeki

Printed in UK by Portland Print

Published by
NOBLE GEMS PUBLICATIONS
www.noblegems.com
info@noblegems.com

TABLE OF CONTENTS

WHITE AND YELLOW
DIAMOND NECKLACE

Courtesy of Graff Diamonds

143.18 CARATS

Preface and Acknowledgments

This book is designed to help the reader acquire a basic knowledge of diamonds and the diamond industry, as well as a deeper understanding of the main factors which determine the value and quality of a diamond. For this new edition, several features have been added. As well as background and historical information, there is a new chapter on natural color diamonds, with full-color photographs showing the remarkable variety and beauty of different types of diamonds. The final chapter tells the story of one of the world's largest diamonds, from the moment it was first discovered through its transformation into a stunning necklace.

I am deeply indebted to Graff Diamonds for their kind permission to reproduce their illustrations from 'The Most Fabulous Jewels In The World' collection, pp. 8, 10, 13, 40, 45, 55, 57, 65, 70, 71, 74, 76-93. I would also like to thank the following individuals and organizations for allowing us to use their illustrations: Arthur Langerman (all images copyright of ©Langerman Diamonds), 48, 50, 52, 56, 58-64, 66-69, 72, 73; De Beers, 25, 32, 39; Gemological Institute of America (GIA), 18, 43, 54; The Royal Asscher® Diamond Company, 31; Laurent Boeki, 22, 25, 28-30, 33-38 and cover; and Anna Moltke-Huitfeldt, 46, 47.

I would also like to extend my thanks to the following for their valuable input and assistance: Natacha Langerman for her advice and help with the section on natural color diamonds; Elizabeth Fisk for her excellent contributions; Talal Shembesh GG for valuable suggestions; Anne-Marie Reeves for sharing her expertise on De Beers and the diamond industry; and Denise Dresner for her invaluable editing and writing.

Marijan Dundek
London, 2015

THE IDOL'S EYE
70.21 CARATS

One of the world's most spectacular historical diamonds,
discovered in the Golconda mines around 1600.

HISTORY OF DIAMONDS

Diamonds are the most prized and highly valued of gemstones. Throughout history they have been admired by royalty and worn as a symbol of strength, courage and invincibility. Over the centuries the diamond acquired unique status as the ultimate gift of love, in myth and reality. It is the hardest known substance yet has the simplest chemical composition, consisting of crystallized carbon, the chemical element that is fundamental to all life. Diamonds come in many colors and their optical properties are stunning. They disperse light into the colors of the rainbow, and sparkle far more than any other gemstone.

First mined in India over 4000 years ago, diamonds were used to decorate religious objects, serve as a talisman against evil and a protector in battle. Buddhists also recognized the deep symbolic significance accorded to diamonds in ancient Buddhist scriptures, including the 'Diamond Sutra' which states that truth is eternal, just like the diamond. Diamonds are also found in the culture and mysticism of Hinduism, Jainism and Tibetan Lamaism. The Sanskrit word 'vajra' – meaning both thunderbolt and diamond – was the name for a small metal weapon having the symbolic nature both of a diamond (able to cut any substance but not be cut itself) and of the thunderbolt (irrepressible force). The Buddhist equivalent, 'dorje', was a talisman in the shape of a four-faceted diamond which represented the sacred Mount Meru, believed to be at the center of the universe. The highly valued Tibetan diamond dzi bead represents the dorje/vajra symbol and bestows diamond-like qualities on its wearer: it can help bring to light the many beautiful or dormant facets within the self, and its brilliance shines on the wearer to illuminate beauty and repel all that is ugly.

In ancient times India was the world's only source of diamonds until the beginning of the 18th century, except for minor deposits found in Kalimantan, Borneo. Most were mined from alluvial deposits along riverbanks. Today the most prized historical diamonds are still known as the 'diamonds of Golconda,' a region located between the lower reaches of the Godavari and Krishna rivers. Golconda diamonds are believed to be the finest and purest of any gemstones. They have a perfect internal crystal structure, exceptional transparency and are without any trace of color.

It is believed that Alexander the Great brought the first diamonds to Europe from India in 327 BC, instigating the expansion of trade routes between Europe and the East.

Ancient Greeks believed diamonds to be 'tears of the gods' and splinters of falling stars. The word 'diamond' is derived from the Greek word 'adamas', meaning invincible, indestructible, and later translated into Latin as 'diamas'.

During the Greco-Roman era, diamonds became a valuable commodity in trade and gradually became a symbol of luxury. Romans were also known to use diamond fragments set in iron as tools which were traded with China and used for carving jade or drilling pearls.

The early diamond trading capital was Venice, where polishing a diamond's facets began in the 1330s. For centuries, Indian diamonds reached first Rome and later Venice by two routes, known collectively as the fabled Silk Route; the southern route was by way of Aden, Ethiopia and Egypt and the northern route was through Arabia, Persia, Armenia and Turkey.

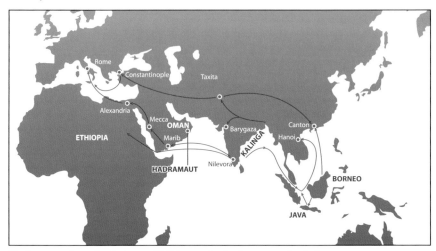

Trade routes from the Orient to Old Europe in the first centuries B.C.

By the late 14th century the art of diamond polishing had spread to Bruges and Paris and later, in the 15th century, Antwerp became the new flourishing diamond center, supplied with rough stones through Lisbon as well as Venice.

In the 17th century the French traveler and diamond merchant, Jean-Baptiste Tavernier, made a series of voyages to India and brought back a number of stupendous diamonds to Europe. London also emerged as an important cutting center at this time, and later took over the role of a major trading center for rough diamonds.

Indian mines became increasingly depleted and by the early 18th century Brazil had surfaced as the next biggest supplier of diamonds. As resources slowly dwindled in Brazil after just 150 years, a new discovery was made in South Africa.

In 1866, a child found an unusual pebble near the Orange River at Cape Colony. This turned out to be a diamond of approximately 21 carats that was named 'Eureka'. The following year another stone was discovered, later confirmed as 83.5 carats, which became known as the 'Star of South Africa'. The largest and most magnificent diamond of all time was found in South Africa in 1905, weighing 3,106 carats and named the 'Cullinan'. The great diamond rush had started, and new deposits continued to be discovered, larger than any the world had ever known. At the beginning of the 20th century South Africa had established itself as the world's top diamond producing country, and was followed by other countries within the African continent and beyond. This marked the start of a new chapter in the history of diamonds.

The Wittelsbach-Graff Diamond
31.06 CARATS

THE DIAMOND INDUSTRY

By the time De Beers was established in 1888, it already owned all diamond mining operations in South Africa. For the next 100 years it maintained its position as the world's foremost producer of rough diamonds; at its peak in the 1980s it accounted for 85% of world production. But its position was soon to be challenged by a global shift in the dynamics of diamond production.

By the 1990s, diamond mining had expanded worldwide, with discoveries of rich deposits in Russia, Australia and Canada. As De Beers saw its dominance begin to wane, other mining companies were emerging as a diamond-producing force in the global marketplace. The largest of these are Alrosa, BHP Bilton, Gem Diamonds, Leviev, Petra, Rio Tinto and Steinmetz among others.

Currently, the major diamond producing countries by volume are Russia, Botswana, DR Congo, Australia, Canada, South Africa and Angola, with the African continent seeing the most development.

The mining of diamonds takes many forms, depending on the environment and terrain, and can be underground, alluvial, deep-sea or open cast. Once mined, rough diamonds are sorted into categories according to their shape, size, color and quality before being sold to specialist diamond cutters and polishers throughout the world.

Traditionally, all the sorting of rough diamonds used to took place in London at the Diamond Trading Company (DTC, part of the De Beers Family of Companies), but this has changed in recent years with the emergence of other trading and processing centers, including Botswana, India, mainland China and Hong Kong.

In southern Africa, newly emerging diamond-mining companies have their own sorting, cutting and polishing operations. This burgeoning industry will help grow the economies of these countries and further their people's prosperity.

The traditional major cutting centers are New York, Tel Aviv, Antwerp and Surat (India), each with different strengths. New York crafts the larger diamonds and Tel Aviv is a major player both as an innovative high-tech manufacturer and as trader. Antwerp remains a key trading center and Surat specializes mainly in smaller diamonds, claiming to process at least 9 out of 10 diamonds polished worldwide.

Secondary cutting and polishing industries also exist in China, Canada, Russia and Thailand, as well as in smaller factories elsewhere.

The early 21st century has thus brought dynamic changes to the diamond trade, which has expanded and evolved into a global and highly organized industry.

The Kimberley Process Certification Scheme

In the late 1990s, the world became aware that rough diamonds from some African countries were being traded in order to fund military conflict by rebel movements. These diamonds became known as 'blood' or 'conflict' diamonds.

In order to combat this, a joint initiative was launched in 2000 by the international diamond industry, governments and NGOs to ensure that diamonds were not used to fund such activities. In 2002 this initiative led to the introduction of the Kimberley Process Certification Scheme (KPCS), a tightly controlled system to ensure that diamonds have been purchased from legitimate sources and comply with specific requirements. By 2009, 75 countries had adopted this UN-mandated scheme.

Today there are strict guidelines regulating production and trade that must be adhered to. All rough diamonds must be accompanied by a Kimberley Process Certificate during their transportation, and detailed records of their provenance must be kept. The industry also adopted a System of Warranties to ensure that consumers buying diamonds are confident of the integrity of their purchase.

The future success of the diamond industry depends on maintaining this integrity throughout. Modern business practice is essential for future growth, and recognizing and meeting responsibilities for business, social, environmental and technical sectors are equally important. As one of Africa's major natural resources, diamonds are helping to transform southern Africa and the lives of its people, while in India the diamond industry continues to employ over 1 million people.

THE GENESIS OF DIAMONDS

The exact origin of diamonds is still something of a mystery even today. It is known that diamonds were created by nature at least 990 million years ago and many are as old as 4.2 billion years. The elemental forces of heat and pressure transformed carbon into diamonds 150-200 km below the surface of the earth. The volcanic mass in which this crystallization took place then thrust upwards and broke through the earth's surface to cool in kimberlite, or lamproite, pipes where diamonds are found today.

Diamonds that were washed away from the original source, through the effects of erosion or water, became known as alluvial (or placer) deposits.

Diamonds can also appear on the earth's surface by other means. For instance, the high-pressure and high-temperature conditions that occur when meteors hit the surface of the earth can create extremely small diamonds, known as nanodiamonds or micro-diamonds. Such nanodiamonds, some scientists suggest, might even pre-date the Solar System, perhaps created during volatile conditions at the birth of the universe.

It is not an easy task to recover gem-quality and industrial diamonds, and approximately 100 to 250 tonnes of ore must be mined and processed from the average kimberlite pipe to produce a one-carat, polished, gem-quality diamond. Thus, it is easy to understand why diamonds are so rare and valuable.

The transformation of a rough diamond requires skilled craftsmen who can unlock and reveal the remarkable beauty within, with all the various colors that range from white and black through to yellow, brown, green, blue, pink and the very rare red.

Today, diamonds are the most mined and carefully graded gems. They are cut with great precision and delicacy and come in many shapes, degrees of quality and prices. Their beauty, mystery and magic shine for millions around the world, and express all that the heart feels but cannot be put into words.

PROPERTIES OF DIAMONDS

Chemical composition: C, crystallized carbon

Crystal system: Isometric (cubic)

Mohs' hardness: 10

Specific gravity: 3.417 – 3.55

Refractive index: 2.417 – 2.419

Transparency: Transparent

Dispersion: 0.044

DIAMOND PRODUCING COUNTRIES AND MAJOR CUTTING CENTERS

Diamonds were mined in India more than 4000 years ago, but the modern industry began with the discovery of diamonds in South Africa in the late 19th century.

◇ Major cutting centers   • Major producing countries

MAJOR PRODUCING COUNTRIES

Russia, Botswana, DR Congo, Australia, Canada, South Africa, Angola, Namibia, Guinea, Ghana, Zimbabwe, Sierra Leone, Central African Republic, Guyana, Lesotho, Tanzania, Brazil, China, Liberia, Indonesia, Togo, Venezuela, Ivory Coast, India.

MAJOR CUTTING CENTERS

Antwerp, New York, Tel Aviv and Surat, followed by China, Dubai UAE, Botswana, South Africa, Australia, Canada, Russia, Thailand, Brazil, Dominican Republic, Germany, United Kingdom, Holland, Haiti, Indonesia, Japan, Malaysia, Malta, Mauritius, North Korea, Philippines, Portugal, South Korea, Sri Lanka, Taiwan, Tanzania, Tunisia, Vietnam.

QUALITY OF DIAMONDS

There are four main factors by which the value and quality of a diamond are determined (popularly called the 4Cs), and any combination of these factors make it possible to evaluate a diamond.

These factors are: **color, clarity, cut and carat**.

COLOR

Color is a very important characteristic of a gemstone and it is one of the key factors to be considered when determining the value of a diamond. The ideal color is the total absence of all body color (colorless) except in fancy color diamonds, such as yellow, pink, blue, green, purple, brown, black and the very rare red, where an intense hue is an asset. A very precise scale of color grading, as defined and developed by the GIA, is universally used today in the diamond trade. The color grade begins with the letter D, representing the rarest and most desirable colorless diamonds, and descends to the letter Z, which has a slight hint of yellow or brown. Diamonds are color graded by comparing them to master stones under controlled lighting and precise viewing conditions.

GIA COLOR GRADING SCALE

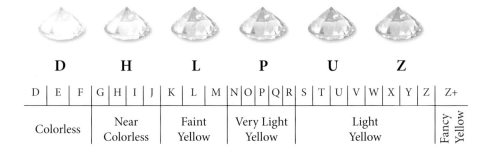

D			H			L			P			U			Z	
D	E	F	G	H	I	J	K	L	M	N	O	P	Q	R	S	T	U	V	W	X	Y	Z	Z+
Colorless			Near Colorless			Faint Yellow			Very Light Yellow				Light Yellow										Fancy Yellow

COLOR GRADING SCALES

Besides the GIA Color Grading Scale, there are a number of others, including:

IGI – International Gemological Institute

AGS – American Gemological Society

CIBJO – The World Jewellery Confederation

HRD Antwerp – Institute of Gemmology

GIA	IGI	AGS	CIBJO		HRD	
D	D	0.0	Exceptional White (+)	D	Exceptional White (+)	D
E	E	0.5	Exceptional White	E	Exceptional White	E
F	F	1.0	Rare White (+)	F	Rare White (+)	F
G	G	1.5	Rare White	G	Rare White	G
H	H	2.0	White	H	White	H
I	I	2.5	Slightly Tinted White (I)	I	Slightly Tinted White	I
J	J	3.0	Slightly Tinted White (J)	J		J
K	K	3.5	Tinted White (K)	K	Tinted White	K
L	L	4.0	Tinted White (L)	L		L
M	M	4.5		M		M
N	N	5.0		N		N
O	O	5.5		O		O
P	P	6.0		P		P
Q	Q	6.5		Q		Q
R	R	7.0		R		R
S	S	7.5	Tinted	S	Tinted	S
T	T	8.0		T		T
U	U	8.5		U		U
V	V	9.0		V		V
W	W	9.5		W		W
X	X			X		X
Y	Y	10.0		Y		Y
Z	Z			Z		Z

CLARITY (DEGREE OF FLAWLESSNESS)

The clarity of a gemstone is assessed by examination of imperfections – that is, inclusions (internal objects) and blemishes (external marks) – under 10x magnification. Almost all diamonds contain minute traces of non-crystallized carbon or small non-diamond crystals, and are nature's fingerprint, making every diamond unique.

Most of such imperfections are not visible to the naked eye and require magnification to be detected. However, the fewer there are, the rarer the gemstone will be. Diamonds without any inclusions or blemishes are exceptionally rare, and rarity affects a diamond's value.

Using the GIA International Diamond Grading System, diamonds are assigned a clarity grade that ranges from flawless (FL) to diamonds with obvious inclusions (I_3).

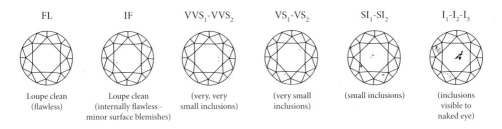

FL	IF	VVS_1-VVS_2	VS_1-VS_2	SI_1-SI_2	I_1-I_2-I_3
Loupe clean (flawless)	Loupe clean (internally flawless - minor surface blemishes)	(very, very small inclusions)	(very small inclusions)	(small inclusions)	(inclusions visible to naked eye)

DEFINITIONS OF CLARITY GRADES ACCORDING TO INTERNAL DEFECTS

FL (flawless) – no inclusions or blemishes of any sort are visible to a skilled grader using 10x magnification

IF (internally flawless) – no inclusions and only blemishes are visible to a skilled grader using 10x magnification

VVS_1 and VVS_2 (very, very slightly included) – inclusions are difficult for a skilled grader to see using 10x magnification

VS_1 and VS_2 (very slightly included) – inclusions are clearly visible under 10x magnification but can be characterized as minor

SI_1 and SI_2 (slightly included) – inclusions are noticeable to a skilled grader using 10x magnification

I_1, I_2 and I_3 (imperfect) – inclusions are obvious under 10x magnification and may affect transparency and brilliance

CLARITY GRADING SCALES

Along with the GIA Clarity Grading Scale there are a number of others illustrated here. These are:

IGI – International Gemological Institute
AGS – American Gemological Society
CIBJO – The World Jewellery Confederation
HRD Antwerp – Institute of Gemmology

GIA	IGI	AGS	CIBJO	HRD
FL	IF	0	Loupe clean	Loupe clean
IF				
VVS_1	VVS_1	1	VVS_1	VVS_1
VVS_2	VVS_2	2	VVS_2	VVS_2
VS_1	VS_1	3	VS_1	VS_1
VS_2	VS_2	4	VS_2	VS_2
SI_1	SI_1	5	SI_1	SI_1
SI_2	SI_2	6	SI_2	SI_2
I_1	I_1	7	Piqué I	P_1
I_2	I_2	8	Piqué II	P_2
		9		
I_3	I_3	10	Piqué III	P_3

CUT

The cut refers to a diamond's proportions and finish, and it is the only one of the 4Cs directly influenced by hand, as the other three are determined by nature. The word 'cut' can also refer to shape (the face-on appearance of the gem) and cutting style (the arrangement of the gem's facets).

A well cut diamond can make light perform in breathtaking ways, resulting in a magnificent display of three important diamond attributes:

Brilliance – the total light reflected from a diamond

Fire – the dispersion of light into the colors of the spectrum

Scintillation – the flashes of light, or sparkle, when a diamond is moved

An understanding of a diamond cut begins with the shape of a diamond, of which there is a wide variety, the most popular being the round brilliant cut. All other shapes are known as fancy shapes.

The proportions of a diamond refer to the relationship between table size, crown angle and pavilion depth. A wide range of proportion combinations are possible, and these ultimately affect the stone's interaction with light.

The finish has two aspects: polish, referring to the overall condition of a gem's facet surface; and symmetry, which refers to the precision of the shape and placement of the facets.

These factors, along with the thickness of a diamond's girdle, affect its overall cut grade.

IDEAL CUT DIAMOND

In 1919, Marcel Tolkowsky developed a mathematical formula for cutting diamonds to precise angles and proportions to gain the best reflection and refraction of light, creating the optimum balance, sparkle and fire of the diamond. The proportions he chose produced a beautiful diamond which became the basis for the 'modern round brilliant cut', also referred to as 'American ideal cut'. Over the years Tolkowsky's proportions were slightly modified, resulting in several variations of that cut. Today the term 'ideal (excellent) cut' refers to the attempt to cut a round diamond into the best proportions to achieve maximum brilliance, fire and scintillation. Ongoing research into cuts suggests that many different combinations of proportions succeed equally well in achieving that degree of excellence.

HEARTS & ARROWS

One such cut is Hearts and Arrows. Also called H&A, these are mostly round diamonds with a superior cutting quality. They display a visual pattern of 8 hearts when looking at the pavilion, and 8 arrows when viewing the stone in the face-up position, while using a Hearts and Arrows loupe.

Image courtesy of IGI

THE FACETS OF A BRILLIANT CUT AND TERMS WHICH ARE APPLIED TO THE SECTIONS OF A DIAMOND

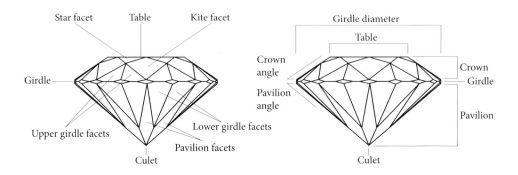

THE REFLECTIVE QUALITIES OF DIAMOND CUT

When a diamond is perfectly cut, light rays from all sides are bent towards the center of the stone and are reflected back through the top in a rainbow blaze of light.

If a diamond is not perfectly cut, light will 'leak' out through the base or sides of the diamond.

In a diamond which is cut too deep, much of the light is reflected to opposite facets at the wrong angle and is lost through the sides. The diamond may appear black in the center.

In a diamond cut too shallow, the light 'leaks' through the bottom and the eye may see a dull reflection.

DIAMOND INSCRIPTIONS AND BRANDING

Diamond inscription is the process of etching a certificate number or name on a diamond's girdle for the purposes of identification and security. The inscription is engraved by a very fine, very precise non-invasive laser beam and is only visible under very high magnification. Laser inscription does not change a diamond's color grade or clarity grade. The practice of inscribing a personal message is becoming increasingly popular.

Branded diamonds guarantee the specific standards for cutting style, beauty and brilliance developed and promoted by the company whose name they bear.

With their Forevermark diamonds, De Beers recently introduced the novel practice of branding diamonds in the middle rather than on the girdle, marking the first major innovation in diamond branding since Lazare Kaplan introduced the first branded and laser-inscribed round diamond (The Lazare Diamond® Ideal Cut) in 1985.

Example of laser inscription on the girdle   *Example of De Beers 'Forevermark' branding*

DIAMOND CUT GRADING SCALES

The table below details the various laboratories and the different grading scales they use; please note that the top grade is not the same for each laboratory.

GIA	IGI	AGS	HRD
Excellent	Excellent - Ideal	Ideal (AGS0)	Excellent
	Excellent	Excellent (AGS1)	
Very Good	Very Good	Very Good (AGS2)	Very Good
Good	Good	Good (AGS3, AGS4)	Good
Fair	Fair	Fair (AGS5, AGS6, AGS7)	Fair
Poor	Poor	Poor (AGS8, AGS9, AGS10)	

AMERICAN AND EUROPEAN STANDARDS FOR IDEAL PROPORTIONS OF A ROUND BRILLIANT CUT DIAMOND

Tolkowsky – Standard American Ideal Cut

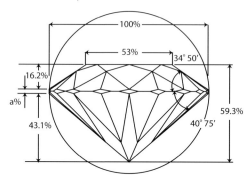

Eppler – Practical Fine Cut (European Cut)

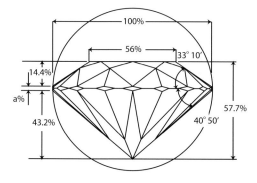

Scan D.N. – Scandinavian Standard Brilliant

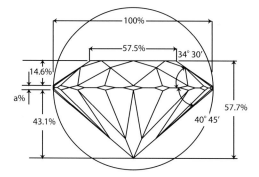

DIAMOND SHAPES

The shape of a diamond is governed by the way it is cut, and good cutting, polishing and proportions are collectively the key to a beautiful gemstone. The earliest shapes of a stone were simple, restricted by the technology of the time. As techniques, knowledge and tools improved, the cuts have become more complex, resulting in the great variety of shapes we see today (as seen in the diagram below).

Point cut

Table cut

Old single cut

Mazarian cut

Peruzzi cut

Old European cut

STANDARD DIAMOND SHAPES

These are the traditional shapes of diamonds generally used today. The most popular among them is the round brilliant cut diamond with its 57 facets (or 58 if the culet is cut and polished).

The shape of a polished diamond is classified as either round brilliant cut, which refers to a round shape, or fancy cut, which refers to any other shape.

There are three different styles of cut:

Round brilliant cut – this is the most familiar cut. Other examples of brilliant cuts are: oval, pear, marquise, and heart. All brilliant cuts have 57-58 facets and are admired for their brilliance and fire.

Step cut – this has a row of facets that resemble the steps of a staircase and is usually four-sided and elongated. The other variations of the same cut are square emerald and Asscher cut.

Mixed cut – this has both brilliant and step-cut facets. Examples of mixed cuts are cushion, radiant and princess cuts.

ROUND BRILLIANT CUT

The round brilliant cut diamond is the most popular diamond shape. It was cut for centuries, but in 1919 Marcel Tolkowsky defined specific angles and proportions which would provide a balanced return of light (brilliance) and dispersion, forming the basis for the modern round brilliant cut diamond.

Round brilliant diamonds are the only shape to have the perfect proportions defined. This shape has set the standard for all other diamond shapes and accounts for more than three-quarters of all diamonds sold today.

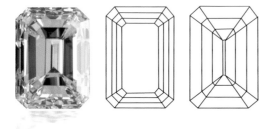

EMERALD CUT

Emerald cut diamonds are among the most popular fancy cuts. A type of step cut, these gemstones have longer lines, are usually less fiery than a round brilliant cut, but also tend to have wider, more dramatic flashes of light. They reveal a classic noted for a subtle beauty and elegance not seen in other cuts. Emerald cut diamonds are available in shapes ranging from square to rectangular.

When choosing the emerald cut it is important to pay attention to the quality of the diamond, and it is better to go for higher quality because both inclusions and lower color are more noticeable in this gemstone.

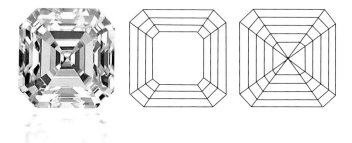

ROYAL ASSCHER CUT

The Asscher cut was developed by Joseph Asscher in 1902 and was the first signature cut to be patented. In 1908 his company was commissioned by the Royal Family to cut the world's largest diamond in history, the 3,106 carat Cullinan diamond.

In 2001 the brothers Edward and Joop Asscher designed and introduced the patented Royal Asscher Cut, with new specifications and additional facets for a more brilliant shine. These diamonds are cut to a 74 facet, step-cut octagon and have a majesty and sophistication all their own, embodying the elegance of an earlier age. It features a small table, high crown, deep pavilion and cut corners, meant to draw the eye into the center of the diamond. These characteristics put its sparkle on a par with the round brilliant cut diamond.

Original Asscher cut diamonds have 58 facets and may still be found in antique jewellery stores and auctions, but they are rare. In 1980 Her Majesty Queen Juliana of Holland granted the Asscher company a 'Royal' prefix for playing such a significant role in the diamond industry, and the Asscher Diamond Company subsequently became Royal Asscher.

Every Royal Asscher cut diamond is laser inscribed with the Royal Asscher logo and an identification number belonging to that particular diamond only. The Royal Asscher cut also comes with independent GIA, AGS and/or HRD certification. (On a GIA report the Asscher cut is referred to as a 'modified square emerald cut'.)

Cushion Cut

Cushion cut diamonds have rounded corners and larger facets to increase their brilliance. It is based on the antique cushion cut, which is a combination of round and square outlines, with a softened square or 'pillow' shape that gives it its name.

This unique cut has been popular for more than a century and is available in shapes ranging from square to rectangular. A fancy cut, it has very romantic connotations and an antique look to it. Modern cushion cut diamonds are also known as 'candlelight diamonds'. These diamonds have a look that evokes romance because of their natural shine and beauty.

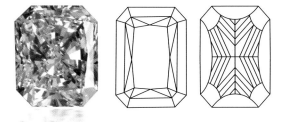

RADIANT CUT

The radiant cut has 70 facets and is known for its cut corners. This cut has the class and elegance of an emerald cut without sacrificing the brilliance of a round brilliant cut. Radiant cut diamonds can vary in their degree of rectangularity. The radiant cut is especially popular for fancy colored diamonds, because the shape, proportions and facet arrangement intensify the color.

The radiant cut is the first rectangular cut to have a complete brilliant facet pattern applied to both the crown and pavilion and, as such, presents a much more dazzling and brilliant diamond than the simple emerald cut.

Squarer shaped radiant cut diamonds are also a popular choice for diamond lovers looking for a very bright and brilliant square cut diamond.

 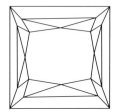 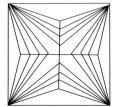

PRINCESS CUT

The princess cut is sometimes referred to as a square modified brilliant, as its faceting style is similar to a round brilliant, with triangular and kite-shaped facets radiating from the center. It combines the brilliance of a round cut with an overall square or rectangular appearance.

Princess cut diamonds can have 49 to 78 facets, but generally have 78 for greater brilliance. It is a relatively new cut and increasingly popular, due to its wonderful characteristics that combine both style and brilliance.

MARQUISE CUT

The typical marquise diamond is a variation of the round brilliant cut, with elongated ends that stretch it into an oval shape. Legend has it that the name derives from the Marquise of Pompadour, and that King Louis XV of France wanted a diamond to be cut in the shape of the marquise's smile.

With 56 facets, the marquise is a slender, striking cut that is ideal for rings. The elongated shape flatters the finger with its regal form and tapering points at both ends.

The marquise cut tends to emphasize the carat weight of the diamond, making it appear much larger than it is, and also has the brilliance and sparkle of a perfect round brilliant cut.

Pear Shape

The pear shape is a fancy cut that is a variation of the traditional round brilliant cut. As such, pear shape cut diamonds are a combination of the oval and the marquise cut, resembling a glittering teardrop.

Pear shape diamonds have good proportions that refract light well and are best set off in a pendant or in a pair of diamond earrings. Pear shapes are also suitable as shoulder stones for a major center stone, or in a cluster around a larger diamond.

The pear shape allows a range of cutting styles, so that the teardrop shape can be wider, slimmer, or cut to perfect proportions, based on personal choice and preferences.

OVAL SHAPE

The oval shaped diamond has a beautiful brilliance very similar to a round diamond except that it is an elliptical variation of the round brilliant, with 56 to 58 facets. The oval cut diamond was created by Lazare Kaplan in the early 1960s. The elongated shape of oval cut diamonds has the unique characteristic of creating a flattering illusion of lengthening the hand. The shape itself presents a larger surface area than a round diamond of the same carat weight, thus giving the appearance of a larger stone.

HEART SHAPE

Heart-shaped diamonds are one of the most attractive of the fancy cut diamonds. They are modified brilliants, as the cut is based on a round brilliant cut.

Heart-shaped diamonds are high-quality diamonds cut into the shape of the universal symbol of love, and are undoubtedly the most romantic.

The skill of the cutter can make a great difference in the beauty of this cut. The 'shape appeal' is especially important with hearts.

It is important to find a heart-shaped diamond with even lobes and a well-defined outline. The lobes should be well-rounded instead of tapering, and clearly defined. The complexity of the shape requires skilled cutting to ensure proper brilliance. Symmetry is a vital consideration for this shape, as the shape needs to have a pleasing, obvious heart silhouette apparent in the setting.

 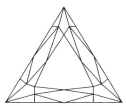 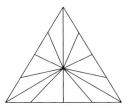

TRILLIANT CUT

The trilliant cut diamond is one of the more unusual diamond cuts and is also known as trillion or trielle cut. Triangular in shape, trilliant cut diamonds can often come with slightly curved sides that create a softer look than the straight-edged trilliant cut diamonds.

The trilliant cut diamond displays a very sharp brilliance and fire if the diamond is cut to the correct depth allowing good scintillation.

Triangular diamonds are most often used as matched side-stone pairs for rings, diamond stud earrings and solitaire pendant necklaces and rings. The exact design can vary and the stone can have 31, or in some versions 44, facets.

THE STAR OF AMERICA
100.57 CARATS

CARAT

The carat is a unit of weight, not size. One carat (1ct) weighs 200 milligrams (1/5 of a gram) and is divided into 100 points, so that a diamond of 50 points is described as half a carat or 0.50 carats. Carat weight is the most obvious factor in determining the value of a diamond, but it is important to remember that two stones of equal size can have very different values depending on the other members of the 4Cs: clarity, color and cut. In addition, it is important to understand that carat weight does not affect the value of diamonds proportionately, and the larger the stone, the more disproportionate the increase in cost per carat.

ROUND BRILLIANT CUT DIAMONDS
WEIGHTS AND CORRESPONDING DIAMETERS

0.03cts 2.0mm	0.05cts 2.5mm	0.07cts 2.7mm	0.10cts 3.0mm	0.15cts 3.4mm
0.20cts 3.8mm	0.25cts 4.1mm	0.30cts 4.5mm	0.40cts 4.8mm	0.50cts 5.2mm
0.65cts 5.6mm	0.75cts 5.9mm	0.85cts 6.2mm	1.00cts 6.5mm	1.25cts 7mm
1.50cts 7.4mm	1.75cts 7.8mm	2.00cts 8.2mm	2.25cts 8.6mm	2.50cts 9.0mm
3cts 9.3mm	4cts 10.2mm	5cts 11.0mm	6cts 11.7mm	7cts 12.4mm

41

DIAMOND GRADING REPORT

A diamond grading report (or certificate) is issued by the gem trade laboratories and is widely used for stones of very fine quality over one carat. The GIA also uses a Diamond Dossier to describe stones under a carat. Smaller diamonds are often certified by reputable shops themselves. The purpose of the grading report is to confirm that the stone is genuine and to evaluate each of the important factors which affect quality, beauty, weight and, consequently, the value. It is also useful for insurance purposes as the information which the report contains is critical to identifying the stone. In addition, each certificate has a unique identification number that can be linked back to the grading laboratory's database.

Among the many different diamond grading laboratories, some of the most reputable and well known are: GIA (Gemological Institute of America), IGI (International Gemological Institute), AGS (American Gemological Society), HRD Antwerp (Institute of Gemmology), IDL (International Diamond Laboratories - Dubai) and the DCLA (Diamond Certification Laboratory of Australia).

Each of these diamond grading laboratories has its own criteria and method of grading loose diamonds, but they are all adapted from the GIA diamond grading system because other labs know that the GIA system is universally accepted.

A certificate from any of these grading laboratories can be considered accurate, reliable and trustworthy.

GIA Certified Diamond Reports provide the following information:

- Date
- Report number
- Laser inscription registry
- Shape and cutting style
- Measurements
- Carat weight
- Color grade
- Clarity grade
- Cut grade
- Finish
- Polish
- Symmetry
- Fluorescence
- Comments
- (Additional) inscription
- Plotting diagram
- GIA color and clarity scales
- GIA cut scale
- Proportion diagram
- Key to symbols
- Security features

DIAMOND GRADING REPORT

SAMPLE OF GIA DIAMOND GRADING REPORT

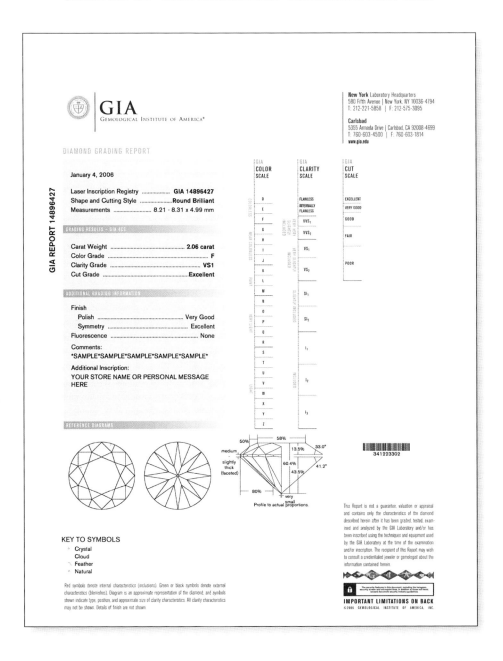

43

DIAMOND FLUORESCENCE

Fluorescence is a phenomenon which causes some 35% of gem-quality diamonds to glow under ultraviolet (UV) light which is abundant in natural daylight and some artificial lighting. This glow lasts only as long as the diamond is exposed to the ultraviolet rays.

In more than 95% of the diamonds that exhibit fluorescence, the color seen is blue, and in rare instances green, yellow, orange, or a combination of these colors.

Fluorescence is caused by the presence of nitrogen or other impurities in the diamond crystal structure and does not have any influence on the hardness or durability of a diamond.

In addition to color, fluorescence also varies by strength – from none, faint and medium to strong and very strong, as described on GIA grading reports. The fluorescence color and its intensity are additional characteristics that can help to identify a specific diamond.

GIA studies have shown that, for the overwhelming majority of diamonds, the strength of fluorescence has no widely noticeable effect on appearance. In fact, many people prefer the appearance of diamonds that have medium to strong fluorescence. In very rare cases (less than 0.2% of fluorescent diamonds seen by the GIA), some diamonds with extremely strong blue fluorescence may appear hazy or oily, and gemstones with such characteristics are slightly less desirable. Diamond fluorescence is a natural phenomenon and is best judged by considering each individual diamond on its own visual merits.

THE FLAME
PEARSHAPE PENDANT 100 CARATS

Courtesy of Graff Diamonds

NATURAL FANCY COLOR DIAMONDS

Natural Fancy Color Diamonds

In the magical world of precious stones, natural fancy color diamonds hold a place of their own, next to their colorless counterparts.

Most diamonds that are extracted from the earth are in the colorless to light yellow range (D to Z grade). Fancy color diamonds or 'fancies' go off this scale and have a deep, distinct and opulent color.

Diamonds of all colors can be found in nature. They are a miracle of nature, revealing themselves in incredibly beautiful shades, hues and colors such as yellow, green, blue, purple, pink, orange, brown, black and – extremely rarely – red. Over 300 colors have been identified so far, however these come in an infinite number of shades and hues.

Unlike colorless and near colorless diamonds which are valued for their lack of color, fancies are valued precisely for the intensity and distribution of theirs. These diamonds are extremely rare and tend to be found mostly as small stones weighing less than a carat.

For every 10,000 colorless diamonds, only one natural color diamond will have made the trip from the depths of the earth to its surface. It is the entirely natural process of geological formation which ensures that each natural color diamond is unique.

The formation of natural color diamonds requires not only the special conditions necessary for the creation of all diamonds, but also the presence of additional trace elements and distortions to the typical diamond crystal. If an element interacts with carbon atoms during the creation of a diamond, the diamond's color can change. Radiation and pressure on a diamond's structure will also have an impact on its color.

COLOR

Color is the most important factor that determines the value of a fancy color diamond. Color is determined by hue, saturation, tone and distribution.

HUE

Hue refers to the dominant color of a stone, such as pink, yellow, blue, green, etc. There can also be modifiers, or tints, which lend more than one hue to a stone, casting it into yet another color category. For instance, a purplish-pink diamond indicates a pink stone with purplish tints. If no such tints are present, the hue of the stone is said to be a pure primary color. It is important to note that white and black have no modifiers.

TONE

Tone represents how light or dark a stone appears, depending on how much brown, black, gray or white is present.

SATURATION

Saturation describes the strength or intensity of the hue or main color. The saturation of lightly toned diamonds can vary from light to intense and vivid. Darker diamonds will range from deep to dark in description.

DISTRIBUTION

Distribution refers to how evenly the color is spread across the body of the gem.

Main Causes of Coloration in Diamonds

Yellow, orange and brown shades in diamonds are caused by the presence of nitrogen. Pure orange, with no hint of brown, is the rarest color and is most likely the result of a combination of nitrogen atoms and structural deformities.

The color of most **blue** diamonds is caused by the presence of boron: the higher the concentration of boron, the more intense the color. Some greenish blue diamonds have been discovered that lack boron; it is thought that their blue color is due to natural radiation that would have been present when they formed. Very rarely, a grayish blue color is caused by the presence of hydrogen.

Pink, purple and red stones owe their color to 'graining', i.e. deformation of the crystal lattice. Different levels of graining will result in different shades Scientists believe graining is due to the tremendous pressures to which diamonds are subjected under the earth's surface. Evidence of graining can be seen at 10x magnification in many Argyle diamonds.

The color of purely **violet** stones is caused by the presence of hydrogen.

Natural **green** diamonds derive their color from exposure to gamma rays deep below the earth's surface over a long period of time, perhaps as long as millions of years. This happens naturally; radiation displaces atoms from their normal position in the crystal lattice. Very rarely, hydrogen may also cause some grayish green stones to form.

Fancy Color Diamond Grading

When fancy colored diamonds are graded by the gem laboratories, a comparison set of master stones is used in combination with printed standard color references.

These tools are necessary to help the grader identify the color, or characteristic color, of the diamond.

The GIA uses specific grades to identify the intensity of colors. These are:

Faint
Very Light
Light
Fancy Light
Fancy
Fancy Intense
Fancy Vivid
Fancy Dark
Fancy Deep

Grading fancy yellow and brown diamonds begins where the D to Z scale ends. A particularly yellow diamond whose color is deeper, more intense or more vivid than a Z color stone moves from the ranks of common colorless diamonds to the rarified realm of fancy colored diamonds.

Colors other than yellow and brown are not graded on the D to Z scale. If a diamond is red, blue, green, or any other hue, even the faintest hint of color qualifies it as a fancy colored diamond.

GIA SAMPLE OF GRADES FOR FANCY YELLOW DIAMONDS

Fancy light yellow   Fancy yellow   Fancy intense yellow   Fancy vivid yellow

Besides the GIA, other reputable gem laboratories have created similar systems to grade fancy color diamonds. However as all the laboratories do not use the same nomenclature, the results often vary.

These laboratories are:

> IGI – International Gemological Institute
> AGS – American Gemological Society
> HRD Antwerp – Institute of Gemmology
> IDL – International Diamond Laboratories - Dubai
> DCLA – Diamond Certification Laboratory of Australia

This system of color diamond grading has been designed according to a methodology based on the color decomposition of diamonds.

Laboratories use approximately 14 hues, 8 grades of saturation, 4 tones and 9 modifiers. These elements can yield very simple results such as 'fancy pink' or 'fancy intense yellow', or much more complex results such as 'fancy dark gray yellowish green (chameleon)' or 'fancy deep brownish greenish yellow'. In all cases, it is important to know that it is always the last word that indicates the main color.

Although this system has been conceived using rigorous scientific criteria, its main problem is the naming of a color: the charts only use color names, either on their own or associated with one another, which is not adequate to express the infinite nuances of colors in the spectrum. In addition to this, the use of only 14 principal colors is too limiting.

More than anything, though, this complex scientific terminology poses a problem for the general public who often believe – wrongly – that a diamond whose certificate provides only one word as a color, will be more precious than a diamond described using a compound color.

Several color diamond specialists have sought to remedy this problem by creating more specific and comprehensible naming systems.

The well-known Argyle mine in Australia, for example, has developed a more complete nomenclature to classify its pink diamonds (P1 to P7, BP1 to BP7, PB1 to PB7) and its brown diamonds, which it has renamed champagne and cognac (C1-C7).

Starting from the principle that all colors can be found in nature, Arthur and Natacha Langerman, who have specialized in diamonds for the past 50 years, have taken the initiative to refer precisely to nature in order to express the infinite variety of diamonds' colors: lime, mint, canary, pumpkin, apricot, chocolate, olive, raspberry, burgundy, sky, steel, lavender… approximately 40 different tones have so far been identified, each declined in five grades. This system has the advantage of allowing the public to grasp more easily and quickly the aspect of a diamond.

TREATED AND SYNTHETIC COLOR DIAMONDS

In light of the growing interest in color diamonds it is important to clear the confusion between treated or synthetic diamonds on the one hand, and natural color diamonds on the other.

Technological developments now allow us to create diamonds of almost any color, either completely artificially or from natural diamonds whose color is unattractive (not clearly defined, yellowish, brownish, etc). Such stones can be manufactured at will, resulting in the production of goods that are the exact contrary of what they are substituting for: diamonds by definition are unique, rare, and exceptional.

A natural color diamond is unique. It is a product of nature, shaped by millions of years of crystallization. Its color is the product of chance and no two natural color diamonds can be identical: it is this uniqueness, this rareness, that gives them their value.

Natural and treated color diamonds are two completely different products that operate on two totally different markets. The intrinsic value and the price of each of these cannot even begin to be compared. And the confusion which now exists – and some would say is willfully created by some manufacturers of treated diamonds – is dangerous since it will impact on consumer confidence.

Natural color diamonds are to be considered like any authentic work of art – a painting by a master, an ancient sculpture, a signed piece of furniture, etc. Treated or synthetic diamonds are only pale imitations, created by the thousands and sold at low cost – just as is the case for copied works of art.

In conclusion:

It is crucial that the buyer have a guarantee that the diamond he/she is purchasing is natural and untreated. Certificates issued by laboratories are an indispensable part of this guarantee.

The identification of a diamond's colors will be more precise if a more realistic approach is adopted, keeping in mind, however, that a brightly colored diamond has a higher value than a paler or darker diamond.

SAMPLE OF GIA NATURAL FANCY COLOR DIAMOND GRADING REPORT

This authoritative report lists the diamond's specifications including its scientific color grade, and guarantees its natural origin.

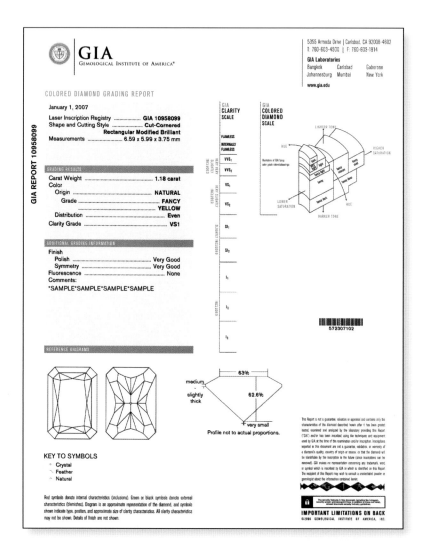

CLARITY

Clarity is not the most important factor for fancy color diamonds, unless inclusions have an impact on the beauty and the life of the stone. Inclusions are crystals that exhibit much the same color as the diamonds and most are not noticeable to the naked eye. To the untrained eye, these crystals blend right in with a diamond's color.

CUT AND SHAPE

For colored diamonds, the only factors that count are color, beauty and sparkle.

Cut refers to a diamond's dimensions and finish and how it interacts with light. Shape refers to the overall outline of the diamond.

The shape will be determined solely on the basis of that which will best amplify the color, which is the most important characteristic in fancy color diamonds. This is why most colored diamonds have a fancy cut; a round cut dissipates color more than a fancy cut. Radiant and cushion are the most popular cuts, followed by oval and pear shapes, heart shape and marquise.

CARAT WEIGHT

Fancy colored diamonds follow the same carat weight grading as their colorless counterparts. The majority of fancy color gems are smaller, usually weighing less than a carat. Large diamonds of 5, 10 or more carats are extremely rare in fancy color diamonds and command astronomically high prices.

After color grade, carat weight has the most effect on price for fancy color gemstones.

PRIMARY HUES OF NATURAL FANCY COLOR DIAMONDS

NATURAL FANCY BLUE DIAMONDS

COLOR

Natural fancy blue diamonds are completely natural and are usually classified as either blue, grayish blue, greenish blue, turquoise or aquamarine.

COLOR FORMATION

The color of blue diamonds is caused by the presence of boron atoms. The higher the concentration of boron, the more intense the color. Some exceptional and very rare turquoise and aquamarine colored diamonds with extremely brilliant appearance have been found to be colored because of their long exposure to natural radiation found in Guyana. And in Argyle blues, which are usually gray blue, the color is related to the presence of hydrogen and also, sometimes but more rarely, to that of nitrogen.

SOURCE

The Cullinan and Premier mines near Pretoria, South Africa are the world's only notable blue diamond producing mines. A small number of extraordinarily deep blue diamonds have also been found in Central Africa, Brazil and Borneo. In the past, some of the most historically famous blue diamonds were sourced from India. The Argyle mine in Australia extracts metallic blue diamonds.

THE IMPERIAL BLUE DIAMOND

39.31 CARATS

Natural Fancy Brown, Champagne Diamonds

COLOR
Natural fancy brown colored diamonds are sometimes referred to as a champagne, lightly tinted brown, cognac or chocolate, depending on their tone (darkness). Their hue is caused by structural distortions in the diamond lattice which modifies their absorption of light. They generally show a hint of greenish, yellowish, orangey or reddish modifying colors.

COLOR FORMATION
Internal parallel grain lines cause the brown color in diamonds. If the brown grain lines exist in a diamond that is also colored yellow by nitrogen impurities, they produce a yellowish brown color.

SOURCE
The Argyle Diamond Mine in Western Australia is the world's largest producer of these stones. Shades ranging from champagne to cognac are found in Australia, Brazil, Borneo, the African continent and Russia.

Natural Fancy Chameleon Diamonds

COLOR
Chameleon diamonds are considered collector's items, consisting of a combination of gray, yellow, olive, orange and green. They can change color from orange to olive and yellow to olive, and vice-versa, depending on the lighting or temperature.

COLOR FORMATION
It is believed that the color-changing effect is due to a higher than normal amount of hydrogen impurities.

SOURCE
Chameleon diamonds are sourced from southeast Asia, mainly China, and also from the Democratic Republic of Congo, central Africa and Brazil.

NATURAL FANCY GRAY DIAMONDS

COLOR

A combination of black and white, gray is a non-spectral color. In their purest form, gray color diamonds come quite close to colorless stones, however they are a highly prized rarity and offer a wondrous range of modifying color combinations in gray, bluish gray, and greenish gray.

Gray appears as a secondary color in most other diamonds, the most common being fancy grayish green, fancy grayish blue, fancy grayish yellow, fancy grayish violet, and fancy grayish purple.

COLOR FORMATION

The color gray is caused by the presence of hydrogen and little or no nitrogen, and bluish gray is generally thought to be caused by boron.

SOURCE

Gray diamonds are sourced from Australia, South Africa, the Democratic Republic of Congo, Russia, India and Brazil.

NATURAL FANCY GREEN DIAMONDS

COLOR

Natural fancy green diamonds are the second rarest gems found in nature after the natural fancy red diamonds. Green diamonds with no other secondary hues or modifiers, depending on intensity and purity of color, can command astronomical prices. They are therefore more highly valued than the yellowish green or greenish yellows. Most green diamonds have either gray, brown, blue, orange or yellow modifiers.

COLOR FORMATION

Green diamonds owe their hue to millions of years of exposure to naturally occurring radiation. Very rarely, hydrogen may be the cause in some grayish green stones.

SOURCE

Green diamonds are sourced from south central Africa, Brazil, British Guyana and Borneo.

NATURAL FANCY OLIVE GREEN DIAMONDS

COLOR
Often confused with the green family, olive occupies a distinct, separate three-dimensional color space next to green. Bordered in this space by grey, black, brown, yellow and green, pure olive stones often have one or more of these modifiers to impart true uniqueness to their hue. Modifiers include grey, green, black, brown and yellow.

COLOR FORMATION
The natural olive green color is caused by the presence of hydrogen impurities.

SOURCE
Beautiful olive diamonds come from Brazil as well as from central Africa, the Democratic Republic of Congo and South Africa.

NATURAL FANCY ORANGE DIAMONDS

COLOR
Prized for their beauty and rarity, orange diamonds are among the most sought after colors. More common, yet still rare, are orange diamonds with a natural color modifier such as brown, yellow, pink or red. Because pure orange is a mixture of the primary colors red and yellow, natural fancy orange diamonds are extremely rare in the lab terminology. Instead, they usually range from reddish orange to yellowish orange.

COLOR FORMATION
Natural fancy orange diamonds are completely natural. Their color is thought to be due to a combination of structural deformities and to the presence of nitrogen in the pure carbon structure, however this has not been verified.

SOURCE
Orange diamonds are predominantly sourced from South Africa, the Democratic Republic of Congo and Russia.

NATURAL FANCY PINK DIAMONDS

COLOR

Pink is one of the rarest and most desirable colors, often associated with roses and natural sea coral. Pure pink colored diamonds with no trace of secondary modifying colors are extremely rare and are usually found in much smaller sizes. Reddish, purplish pink, brownish pink, grayish pink, and orangey pink are the secondary hues found in natural fancy pink diamonds.

COLOR FORMATION

Pink color is caused by a process known as 'plastic deformation', a slipping or distortion of the atomic lattice. Tremendous pressure exerted on a diamond deep in the earth can abnormally compress its structure, creating graining and resulting in red, pink, purple or brown stones. Evidence of graining can be seen under 10x magnification in many Argyle pink and chocolate diamonds.

SOURCE

Today, the Argyle mine in northwestern Australia is famous for the number of pinks it produces, and especially for generating the hugely coveted full-bodied hot pinks. Much lighter pink diamonds have been sourced from India in the past, and today Borneo, China, Brazil, Guinea, Angola, South Africa and Tanzania have been known to produce some notable pink diamonds in small quantities.

PRINCESS ROSE

12.82 CARATS

Natural Fancy Purple Diamonds

COLOR
As is the case for orange diamonds, pure purple colored diamonds are almost nonexistent in the lab terminology, since purple is made of pink and blue. One will more often see purple diamonds described as pinkish purple. Often confused with the secondary color violet, purple is a dominant and rare hue in natural color diamonds. These diamonds tend to have gray or pinkish modifiers.

COLOR FORMATION
The purple color is caused by the internal grain formation.

SOURCE
Purple diamonds are most often sourced from Russia.

NATURAL FANCY RED DIAMONDS

COLOR
Red diamonds are the rarest of the colored diamond collection and only a handful have ever received the grade of fancy red, a red diamond in its purest form.

COLOR FORMATION
Red color is caused by a process known as 'plastic deformation', a slipping or distortion of the atomic lattice. There are brownish red, pinkish red and purplish red diamonds, but these stones are generally rare and their prices reflect their scarcity on the market.

SOURCE
Red diamonds tend to be found in small sizes in Australia, Brazil and Africa.

Natural Fancy Violet Diamonds

COLOR
Natural pure violet diamonds are extremely rare and belong to the purple diamond family. Pure violet with no secondary hue is almost nonexistent and such gems will appear only in small sizes. The violet usually appears with gray or blue as a secondary hue; such stones can therefore be violet, fancy bluish violet or fancy grayish violet.

COLOR FORMATION
It is the presence of hydrogen that produces unique violet hues. They are found in a combination of blue diamonds and purple diamonds, and come in different hues and intensity.

SOURCE
Violet diamonds are sourced from the Argyle mine in Australia as well as from Russia.

NATURAL FANCY WHITE DIAMONDS

COLOR

True white diamonds should not be confused with colorless diamonds as there is an inherent snow-white color to this gemstone. White diamonds differ from colorless in that they are not clear. Pure whites with no secondary colors are rare and highly desirable to dealers and collectors. White diamonds can have a brownish, bluish, yellowish or grayish appearance.

COLOR FORMATION

The fancy white diamond's color may be due to nitrogen and a high concentration of submicroscopic inclusions that scatter light, yielding a translucent 'milky' white color. The nature of these inclusions is unknown. White diamonds are sometimes called 'opalescent' because the dispersion of the light looks somewhat similar to that of opals.

SOURCE

Fancy white diamonds are sourced from the Democratic Republic of Congo, Zimbabwe and central Africa.

The Empress Rose Diamond

70.39 CARATS

THE DREAM DIAMOND NECKLACE

157.65 CARATS

Natural Fancy Black Diamonds

COLOR
Natural black diamonds look striking and dramatic. They are not transparent and do not show 'fire' (flashes of color), but can be exceptionally impressive. Black diamonds may show white or gray inclusions that make them very unique.

COLOR FORMATION
The color in black diamonds is caused by a myriad of graphite inclusions, and some stones have been found to contain trace elements of nitrogen and hydrogen. It is believed that some of the black diamonds fell to the earth as meteorites.

SOURCE
Black diamonds are sourced from Brazil, South Africa, the Central African Republic and Borneo.

NATURAL FANCY YELLOW DIAMONDS

COLOR

Natural yellow diamonds are the most familiar of all colored diamonds. Those with more depth of color than Z on the GIA diamond grading scale fall into the fancy color diamond range. Because of their pleasing yellow color, these stones are frequently associated with bright sunlight, cheerfulness, joy, prosperity and happiness.

Diamonds referred to as canary yellow are the rarest type of yellow diamonds. The most popular hues are the fancy intense and fancy vivid with a bright, pure shade and no hints of green, brown or red to darken the stone.

The secondary shades of fancy yellow diamonds are green and orange, and the pure dark tones are brownish or grayish.

COLOR FORMATION

The color in yellow diamonds is due to the presence of nitrogen in the structure of the crystal. In the formation of most yellow diamonds, a few atoms of nitrogen are substituted for carbon. These imperfections interact with light to tint the stones yellow or brown.

SOURCE

Large gem quality diamonds with beautiful intense yellow color have been discovered and mined primarily in South Africa, but also in other African countries, in Brazil, Russia, Australia and India.

Multicolored Diamond Necklace

242.35 CARATS

The Birth
of a Diamond

The Lesotho Promise

DISCOVERY

One day in August 2006, at the Letseng diamond mine high in the mountains of the tiny Kingdom of Lesotho, an amazing discovery was made. The earth had given up one of its rarest treasures – a huge diamond had come to the end of one journey, traveling from deep beneath the earth's crust to the surface, and was at the start of another – its transformation from a rough stone into 26 perfectly cut flawless diamonds.

Named the Lesotho Promise, the diamond was 603 carats in the rough and weighed 120 grams (or 4.2 oz). It was an immensely complicated diamond, with some irregularities, however its color was of the top grade. It was the 15th largest diamond and the 10th largest white diamond the world had ever known.

Diamonds were created by elemental forces deep beneath the earth's crust

ACQUISITION

Jeweller extraordinaire Laurence Graff, who recognized the huge significance of this rare stone, considered it a challenge and decided to buy it. His was the winning bid at the auction of the stone, and thus the Lesotho Promise was acquired by the internationally renown jewellery company Graff Diamonds, via its subsidiary and manufacturing arm, South African Diamond Corporation (Safdico). "I am literally holding a piece of history in my hands," Mr. Graff said at the time.

The Letseng mine in Lesotho where the Lesotho Promise was found

Transformation

Many months of close analysis and examination followed, with a team of 35 people using the latest computer technology to study every aspect of the stone in order to maximize its potential when it would be cut. Experts used a scanner adapted from medical research equipment that was enlarged to accommodate the outsized stone.

As the rough stone contained inclusions, it was decided to cut it into several major stones, rather than a single large stone, and to use only the most beautiful and interesting shapes that would do justice to such a rare and important diamond. The team planned every detail of how facets of the diamonds would align with each other to send light traveling through the stone, releasing its fire and sparkle. They then worked out the best combination of cuts, skirting around the inclusions to achieve optimum yield and beauty.

After all possible options had been analyzed and considered, the long and painstaking process of cutting the diamond could finally begin. The last phase of the diamond's long journey was underway.

A computer-generated view through the stone, showing possible gem combinations

CUTTING

Since every diamond has its own unique characteristics, varying in size, shape, color and clarity, each presents a fresh challenge to the master cutter who will turn the raw stone into a scintillating gem.

Cutting a diamond is a delicate work of art that requires a craftsman's imagination, patience and skill – qualities that are even more essential when the stone is particularly large and complex.

In May 2007, using software, tools and cutting machines developed specially for the Lesotho Promise, the first cut was made. No one had ever before cut a stone of this size and complexity using such advanced technology.

The first cut

The finished diamonds

FINISHING

After the cutting process was complete, each diamond was painstakingly polished using instruments impregnated with diamond dust, the only material capable of polishing a diamond to its full radiance.

The Lesotho Promise yielded 26 'D' color flawless diamonds, ranging from 0.52 carats to 76.41 carats and weighing a total of 223.35 carats. The rest of the original stone – 379.65 carats – either could not be used or was lost in the cutting process.

Each of the diamonds is laser inscribed on the girdle with the Graff logo and a unique GIA identification number. Additionally, each diamond was inscribed with its own Lesotho Promise number.

Polishing the final gems

PEAR SHAPE

76.41 CARATS

HEART SHAPE

43.12 CARATS

ROUND BRILLIANT

27.03 CARATS

Emerald Cut
20.05° CARATS

And so, the rough stone that had begun its life deep in the rece[...] its way to the surface and tumbled down the chute of the Letse[...] in Antwerp with the most advanced technology, and finally ha[...] skill and care, had now reached the end of its journey – transfo[...] fabulous necklace for all to admire.

THE LESOTHO PROMISE NECKLACE

223.35 CARATS

Courtesy of Graff Diamonds

International Organizations and Gem Trade Laboratories

ADGL – Australian Diamond Grading Laboratory
www.adgl.com.au

AGL – American Gemological Laboratories
www.aglgemlab.com

AGS – America Gemological Society
www.americangemsociety.org

AGSL – American Gem Society Laboratories
www.agslab.com

AGTA – American Gem Trade Association
www.agta.org

AIGS – Asian Institute of Gemological Sciences
www.aigsthailand.com

AWDC – Antwerp World Diamond Centre
www.awdc.be

BG – Gemmological Institute (BGGI), Beijing P.R. China
www.bggi.org

BGI – British Gemmological Institute
www.bgiuk.com

BJA – The British Jewellers' Association
www.bja.org.uk

CGA – Canadian Gemmological Association
www.canadiangemmological.com

CGL – Central Gem Laboratory, Japan
www.cgl.co.jp

CIBJO – The World Jewellery Confederation
www.cibjo.org

DCLA – Diamond Certification Laboratory of Australia
www.dcla.com.au

DDE – Dubai Diamond Exchange
www.dde.ae

DEL – German Diamond & Gemstone Laboratories Idar-Oberstein
www.gemcertificate.com

DGemG – German Gemmological Association
www.dgemg.com

GAAJ – Gemmological Association of All Japan Co., Ltd.
www.gaaj-zenhokyo.co.jp

GAHK – The Gemmological Association of Hong Kong
www.gahk.org

Gem Scan International – Canada
www.gemscan.com

Gem-A – The Gemmological Association of Great Britain
www.gem-a.com

GGTL – Laboratories - Liechtenstein
www.ggtl-lab.org

GIA – Gemological Institute of America World Headquarters
www.gia.edu

GII – Gemmological Institute of India
www.giionline.com

GIT – Gem & Jewellery Institute of Thailand
www.git.or.th

GJEPC – Export Promotion Council of India
www.gjepc.org

Gubelin Gem Lab Ltd.
www.gubelingemlab.ch

HKJMA – Hong Kong Jewelry
Manufacturers' Association
www.jewelry.org.hk

HRD Antwerp – Institute of
Gemmology
www.hrdantwerp.be

IBGM – Instituto Brasileiro de Gemas
& Metais Preciosos
www.gemologia.ibgm.com.br

ICA – International Colored
Gemstone Association
www.gemstone.org

IDC – International Diamond Council
www.internationaldiamondcouncil.org

IDL – International Diamond
Laboratories - Dubai
www.diamondlab.org

IDMA – International Diamond
Manufacturers Association
www.idma.net

IGE – Instituto Gemologico Espanol
www.ige.org

IGI – International Gemological
Institute
www.igiworldwide.com

Langerman Diamonds
www.langerman-diamonds.com

LFG – Laboratoire Français de
Gemmologie
www.laboratoire-francais-gemmologie.fr

NAG – The National Association of
Goldsmiths
www.jewellers-online.org

NCDIA – Natural Color Diamond
Association
www.ncdia.com

O.GEM.G – Österreichische
Gemmologische Gesellschaft
www.gemmologie.at

RAPAPORT
www.rapnet.com

SGL – Solitaire Gemmological
Laboratories
www.solitaire-labs.com

SSEF – Swiss Gemmological Institute
www.ssef.ch

WDC – World Diamond Council
www.worlddiamondcouncil.com

WFDB – World Federation of
Diamond Bourses
www.wfdb.com

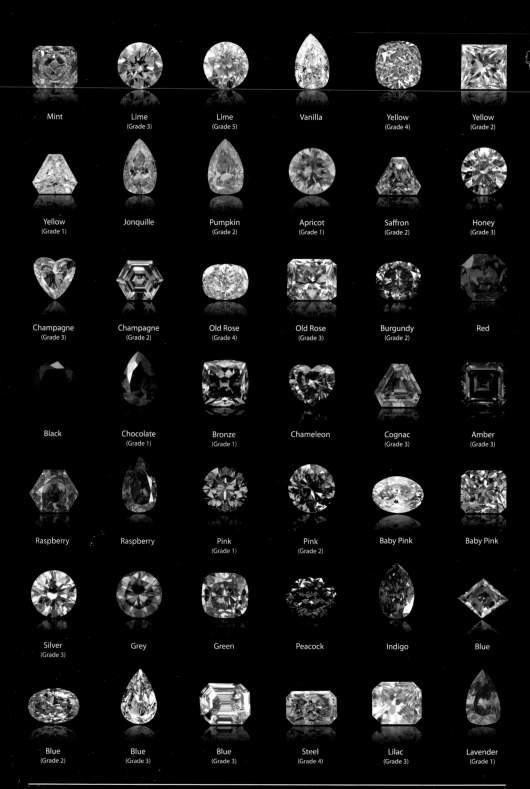

Mint	Lime (Grade 3)	Lime (Grade 5)	Vanilla	Yellow (Grade 4)	Yellow (Grade 2)
Yellow (Grade 1)	Jonquille	Pumpkin (Grade 2)	Apricot (Grade 1)	Saffron (Grade 2)	Honey (Grade 3)
Champagne (Grade 3)	Champagne (Grade 2)	Old Rose (Grade 4)	Old Rose (Grade 3)	Burgundy (Grade 2)	Red
Black	Chocolate (Grade 1)	Bronze (Grade 1)	Chameleon	Cognac (Grade 3)	Amber (Grade 3)
Raspberry	Raspberry	Pink (Grade 1)	Pink (Grade 2)	Baby Pink	Baby Pink
Silver (Grade 3)	Grey	Green	Peacock	Indigo	Blue
Blue (Grade 2)	Blue (Grade 3)	Blue (Grade 3)	Steel (Grade 4)	Lilac (Grade 3)	Lavender (Grade 1)

DIAMONDS